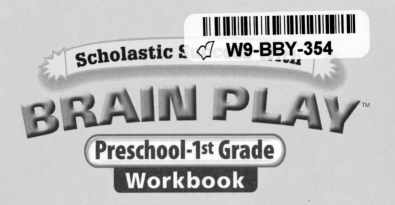

BRAIN PLAY™

Preschool-1st Grade
Workbook

NEW YORK • TORONTO • LONDON • AUCKLAND • SYDNEY
MEXICO CITY • NEW DELHI • HONG KONG • BUENOS AIRES

Acknowledgments

From *Scholastic Success With Math Workbook, Grade 1*. Published by Scholastic Professional
Books/Scholastic Inc. Copyright © 2002 by Scholastic Inc. Reprinted with permission.

From *Scholastic Success With Reading Workbook, Grade 1*. Published by Scholastic Professional
Books/Scholastic Inc. Copyright © 2002 by Scholastic Inc. Reprinted with permission.

From *Scholastic Success With Writing Workbook, Grade 1*. Published by Scholastic Professional
Books/Scholastic Inc. Copyright © 2002 by Scholastic Inc. Reprinted with permission.

From *Scholastic Success With Grammar Workbook, Grade 1*. Published by Scholastic Professional
Books/Scholastic Inc. Copyright © 2002 by Scholastic Inc. Reprinted with permission.

Interior illustrations by Jon Buller, Reggie Holladay, Anne Kennedy,
Kathy Marlin, Bob Masheris, Sherry Neidigh, and Carol Tiernon
Interior design by Quack & Company

ISBN 0-439-82360-9

9 10 23 11 10 09 08 07 06

Table of Contents

READING
COMPREHENSION

Circus Clowns

 *The **main idea** tells what the whole story is about.*

Today I went to the circus. My favorite part of the circus was the clowns. Clowns can do funny tricks. A clown named Pinky turned flips on the back of a horse. Fancy Pants juggled balls while he was singing a funny song. Happy Hal made balloons into animal shapes. Then twelve clowns squeezed into a tiny car and rode away.

Color in the ball that tells the main idea.

Pinky rides a horse.

Balloons can be shaped like animals.

Clowns can do funny tricks.

Clowns drive tiny cars.

Fancy Pants sang a song.

Going to Grammy's

Kelly is going to spend the night with her grandmother. She will need to take her pajamas, a shirt, and some shorts. Into the suitcase go her toothbrush, toothpaste, and hairbrush. Grammy told her to bring a swimsuit in case it was warm enough to swim. Mom said to pack her favorite pillow and storybooks. Dad said, "Don't forget to take Grammy's sunglasses that she left here last week." Now Kelly is ready to go!

1. Color the things that Kelly packed in her suitcase.

Fun at the Farm

 Story events that can really happen are **real.** *Story events that are make-believe are* **fantasy.**

Read each sentence below. If it could be real, circle the picture. If it is make-believe, put an X on the picture.

 The green tractor ran out of gas.

 The newborn calf walked with wobbly legs.

 The goat and the sheep got married by the big tree.

Two crickets sang "Mary Had a Little Lamb."

 Horses sat on the couch and watched TV.

 Rain made the roads muddy.

 Four little ducks swam in the pond.

 The farmer's wife baked a pumpkin pie.

Ready for School

Sequencing *means putting the events in a story in the order they happened.*

Tara could hardly wait for school to start. Mom drove her to the store to buy school supplies. They bought pencils, crayons, scissors, and glue. When Tara got home, she wrote her name on all of her supplies. She put them in a paper sack. The next day, Tara went to school, but the principal told her and the other children to go back home. A water leak had flooded the building. Oh no! Tara would have to wait another whole week!

Number the pictures in the order that they happened in the story.

Swimming Lessons

Sequencing *means putting the events in a story in the order they happened.*

Last summer I learned how to swim. First, the teacher told me to hold my breath. Then I learned to put my head under water. I practiced kicking my feet. While I held on to a float, I paddled around the pool. Next, I floated to my teacher with my arms straight out. Finally, I swam using both my arms and my legs. I did it! Swimming is fun! This summer, I want to learn to dive off the diving board.

Number the pictures in the order that they happened in the story.

My Monster

Be sure to read directions carefully. Look for key words like circle, underline, *and* color.

I saw a scary monster who lived in a cave. He had shaggy fur and a long, striped tail. He had ugly, black teeth. His three horns were shaped like arrows. His nose was crooked. One of his feet was bigger than the other three. "Wake up! Time for breakfast," Mom said. Oh, good! It was only a dream.

Follow the directions.

1. What did the monster's tail look like? Circle it.

2. What did the monster's teeth look like? Draw a box around them.

3. What did the monster's nose look like? Underline it.

4. Which one of these is the correct picture of the monster? Draw a cave around him.

Polly Want a Cracker?

Have you ever heard a parrot talk? Parrots are able to copy sounds that they hear. You can train a parrot to repeat words, songs, and whistles. But a parrot cannot say words that it has never heard. People can use words to make new sentences, but a parrot cannot.

Read each sentence. If it is true, color the parrot under True. If it is false, color the parrot under False.

	True	False

1. You could teach a parrot to sing "Happy Birthday."

2. You could ask a parrot any question, and it could give the answer.

3. A parrot could make up a fairy tale.

Who Am I?

Use details from the story to make decisions about the characters.

Circle the picture that answers the riddle.

1. I have feathers. I also have wings, but I don't fly. I love to swim in icy water. Who am I?

2. I am 3 weeks old. I drink milk. I cry when my diaper is wet. Who am I?

3. I live in the ocean. I swim around slowly, looking for something to eat. I have six more arms than you have. Who am I?

4. I am an insect. If you touch me, I might bite you! I make tunnels under the ground. I love to come to your picnic! Who am I?

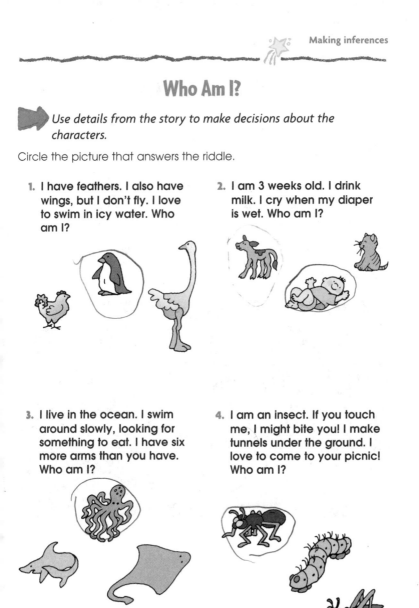

What Will Sam Do?

One day, Sam was riding his bike to the baseball game. He had to be on time. He was the pitcher. Just ahead, Sam saw a little boy who had fallen off his bike. His knee was bleeding, and he was crying. Sam asked him if he was okay, but the boy couldn't speak English. Sam knew the boy needed help getting home. If he stopped to help, he might be late for the game. Sam thought about it. He knew he had to do the right thing.

What do you think Sam did next? There are two paths through the maze. Draw a line down the path that shows what you think Sam did next.

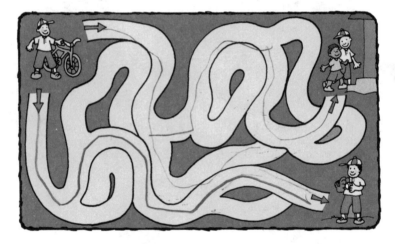

Twins

Holly and Polly are twins. They are in the first grade. They look just alike, but they are very different. Holly likes to play softball and soccer. She likes to wear her hair braided when she goes out to play. She wears sporty clothes. Recess is her favorite part of school. Polly likes to read books and paint pictures. Every day she wears a ribbon in her hair to match her dress. Her favorite thing about school is going to the library. She wants to be a teacher some day.

Look at the pictures of Holly and Polly. Their faces look alike. Circle the things in both pictures that are different from each other.

Soldier Dads

Juan's dad and Ann's dad are
soldiers. Juan's dad is a captain in
the Navy. He sails on the ocean
in a large ship. Ann's dad is a
pilot in the Air Force. He flies a jet.
Juan and Ann miss their dads when
they are gone for a long time. They
write them letters and send them
pictures. It is a happy day when
their dads come home!

Draw a ☺ in the column under the correct dad.
Some sentences may describe both dads.

	Juan's dad	Ann's dad	Both dads
1. He is a captain.			
2. He works on a ship.			
3. Sometimes he is gone for a long time.			
4. He is a pilot.			
5. His child writes to him.			
6. He is in the Air Force.			
7. He is in the Navy.			
8. It is a happy time when he comes home.			
9. He flies a jet.			
10. He is a soldier.			

Oops!

In a story, there is usually a reason something happens. This is the cause. What happens as a result is the effect.

Sandy went on a vacation in the mountains with her parents and little brother Austin. They were staying in a small cabin without any electricity or running water. It was fun to have lanterns at night and to bathe in the cold mountain stream. The biggest problem for Sandy was she missed her best friend, Kendra. Sandy found her dad's cell phone and called Kendra. They talked for nearly an hour! When Sandy's dad went to call his office, the cell phone was dead. He was NOT a happy camper!

Draw a line to match the first part of each sentence to the second part that makes it true.

1. Sandy used lanterns at night because

2. Sandy and Austin bathed in a stream because

3. Sandy felt better about missing Kendra because

4. Sandy's dad could not call his office because

she talked to her on the cell phone.

the cabin had no running water.

the cabin had no electricity.

the cell phone was dead.

School Rules

It is important to follow the rules at school. Read each rule below. Find the picture that shows what would happen if students DID NOT follow that rule. Write the letter of the picture in the correct box.

1. You must walk, not run, in the halls.

2. Do not chew gum at school.

3. Come to school on time.

4. When the fire alarm rings, follow the leader outside.

5. Listen when the teacher is talking.

6. Keep your desk clean.

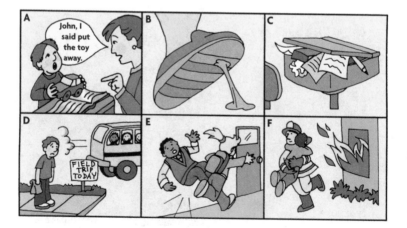

Miss Ticklefoot

I love Miss Ticklefoot. She is my first-grade teacher.

To find out more about her, read each sentence below. Write a word in each blank that tells how she feels. The Word Box will help you.

Word Box

sad	scared	silly	worried	happy	surprised

1. Miss Ticklefoot smiles when we know the answers.

   happy

2. She is concerned when one of us is sick.

   worried

3. She makes funny faces at us during recess.

   silly

4. She cried when our fish died.

   sad

5. She jumps when the fire alarm rings.

   scared

6. Her mouth dropped open when we gave her a present!

   surprised

19

A Fable

A fable is a story that teaches a lesson. This fable was written many, many years ago.

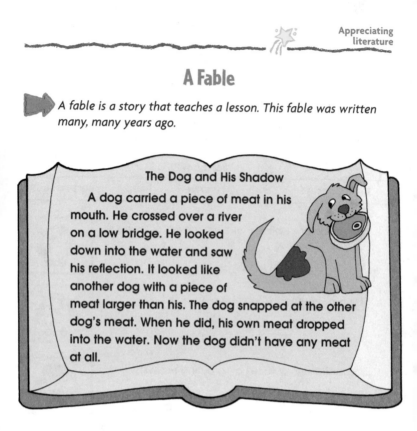

The Dog and His Shadow

A dog carried a piece of meat in his mouth. He crossed over a river on a low bridge. He looked down into the water and saw his reflection. It looked like another dog with a piece of meat larger than his. The dog snapped at the other dog's meat. When he did, his own meat dropped into the water. Now the dog didn't have any meat at all.

Draw a box around the lesson that the story teaches:

1. Two dogs are better than one.

2. Don't be greedy. Be happy with what you have.

TRADITIONAL MANUSCRIPT

A–M

Trace and write.

A B C D

E F G H I

J K L M

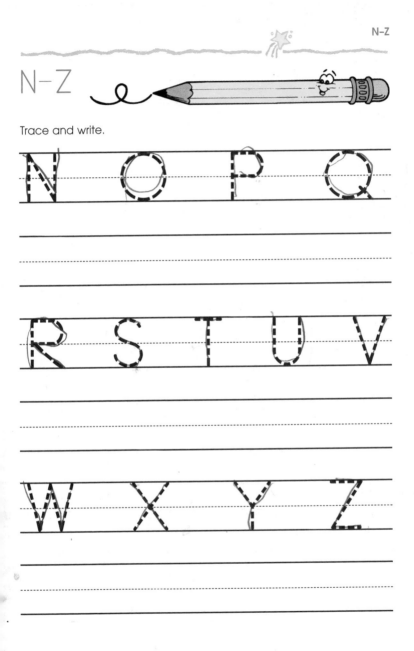

N–Z

Trace and write.

N O P Q

R S T U V

W X Y Z

a–m

Trace and write.

a   b   c

d   e   f

g   h

j   k   l

m

n–z

Trace and write.

n   o   p

q   r   s

t   u   v

w   x   y

z

1-5

Trace and write.

6-10

Trace and write.

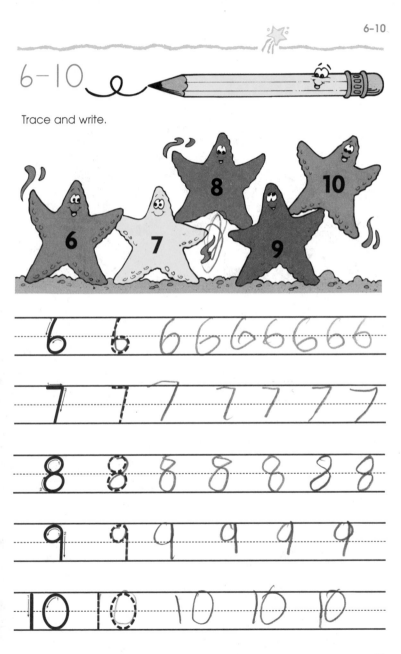

Number Words

Trace and write.

1 one

2 two

3 three

4 four

5 five

More Number Words

Trace and write.

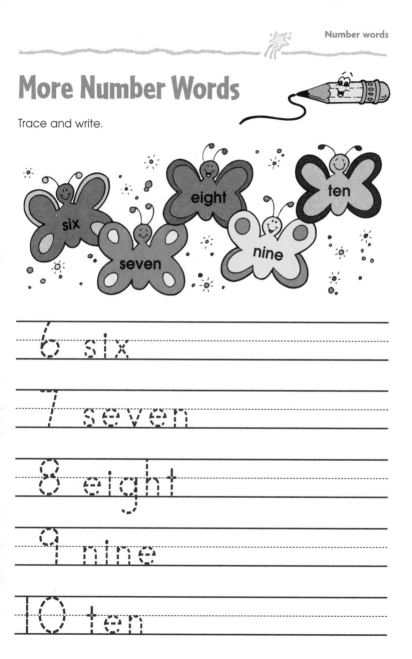

six

seven

eight

nine

ten

6 six

7 seven

8 eight

9 nine

10 ten

GRAMMAR

Capitalizing First Word

A sentence always begins with a capital letter.

Copy each sentence correctly on the line.

1 the cat sat.

---

2 the dog sat.

---

3 i see the cat.

---

4 i can see.

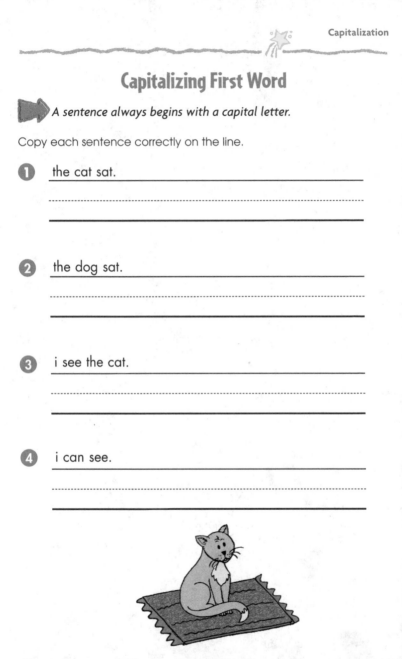

Capitalizing Special Names

 The names of people, places, and pets are special. They begin with capital letters.

Circle each special name. Draw a line under each capital letter in each name.

1 I am Pam.

2 I sit on Ant Hill.

3 Ron likes the lake.

4 He likes Bat Lake.

Read the special names in the box.
Write a special name for each picture.

| Spot   Hill Street |

5 _____

6 _____

Capitalizing Names and First Words

The first word in a sentence starts with a capital letter. Sometimes words that name a person, place, or thing begin with a capital letter.

Read the sentences. Circle the words that are capitalized.

1 The goats Gruff have a problem.

2 They do not like the Troll.

3 His name is Nosey.

4 He is big and bad.

Draw a line to match each sentence as to why the underlined word is capitalized.

5 Dan and <u>Pam</u> like the play.

First word in a sentence.

6 <u>They</u> will read it Jim.

Names a person, place, to or thing.

34

Capitalizing I

Always write the word **I** with a capital letter.

Read the sentences. Write **I** on the line.

1 ___I___ will ride.

2 ___I___ will swim.

3 Mom and ___I___ will sing.

Capitalizing Titles

Important words in a title are capitalized.

Read the titles. Circle all the words that should be capitalized.

1 look at the stars!

2 the moon shines at night

3 we see planets

4 many moons shine

5 night and day

Read each set of titles. Draw a line under the correct title.

6 The Sun in the Sky

the sun in the sky

7 See the stars!

See the Stars!

Periods

 A telling sentence ends with a period.

Circle the period at the end of each sentence.

1 I see Jan.　　　　**2** I go with Jan.

3 We see Dan.　　　　**4** I go with Dan and Jan.

Draw a line under the last word in each sentence.
Add a period to each sentence.

5 We go to <u>school</u>.　　**6** We like <u>school</u>.

Naming Words

 *A naming word names a person, place, or thing.*

Read each sentence. Draw a line under the word or words that name the person, place, or thing in each sentence.

1 The pig is big.

2 The pan is hot.

3 Pam hid.

4 Can you run up the hill?

Draw a line from each sentence to the picture that shows the naming word in that sentence.

5 The sun is hot.

6 Sam ran and ran.

7 Is the cat fat?

Naming Words

 *A naming word names a person, place, or thing.*

Read each sentence. Draw a line under the naming word.

1 We play at school.　　**2** The ball is fast.

3 The girl kicks.　　**4** The friends run.

Look at each box. Circle the naming word that belongs in that box.

Person	Place	Thing
girl	ball	Pam
school	Bill	man
ball	school	ball

Naming Words

 A naming word names a person, place, or thing.

Read each sentence. Draw a line under the word or words that name the person, place, or thing in each sentence.

1 The pot is big.   **2** The pan is big.

3 See the top?   **4** Jim can mop.

Draw a line from each sentence to the picture that shows the naming word in that sentence.

5 The pot is hot.

6 See the pan?

7 Jim is fast.

Action Words

 An action word tells what happens.

Read each sentence. Circle the word that tells what happens.

1 The hen sits.

2 The cat ran.

3 Pam hid.

4 The dog naps.

Read the words. Use the words to finish the sentences.

run	see

5 I will _____ up the hill.

6 I _____ a big pig.

Action Words

An action word tells what happens.

Look at the pictures. Read the action words in the box.
Write the correct action word on the line.

talk

play

dance

run

1 Sue and Al _____play_____ ball.

2 The bears _____ .

3 Rabbit and Pig _____ .

4 Tami and Lee _____ fast.

Describing Words

A describing word tells more about a person, place, or thing.

Look at each picture. Circle the words that tell about it.

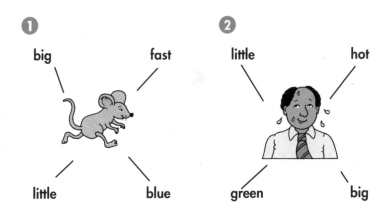

1

big   fast

little   blue

2

little   hot

green   big

Draw a line between each sentence and the picture that shows what it describes.

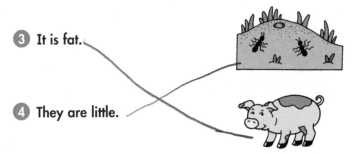

3 It is fat.

4 They are little.

Word Order

Words in a sentence must be in an order that makes sense.

Read each group of words. Write them in the right order on the lines.

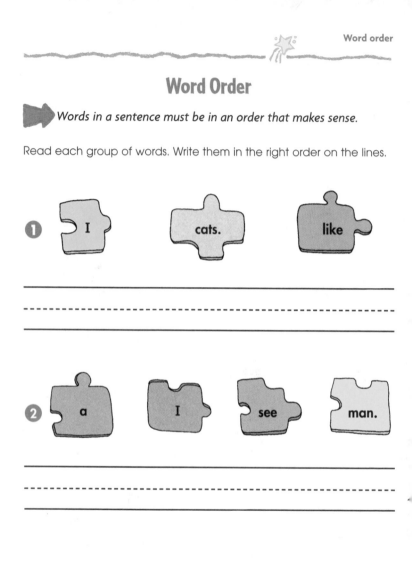

1 I   cats.   like

_____

- -

_____

2 a   I   see   man.

_____

- -

_____

Word Order

Words in a sentence must be in an order that makes sense.

These words are mixed up. Put them in order.
Then write each sentence.

1 snow. bear likes This

This bear likes
snow.

2 water cold. The is

The water is
cold.

3 fast. The runs bear

The bear
runs fast.

Simple Sentences

A sentence tells a complete idea.

Circle who or what each sentence is about.

1 Pam ran.

2 Dan hops.

3 The cat sits.

4 The van can go.

Draw a line from each sentence to the picture of who or what the sentence is about.

5 Jan is hot.

6 The hat is on top.

7 The man sat.

46

Simple Sentences

 A sentence tells a complete idea.

Circle each sentence.

1 Bill
(Bill paints.)

2 likes to read
(Tom likes to read.)

3 plants flowers
(Pat plants flowers.)

Question Sentences

Question sentences ask something.

Draw a line under each sentence that asks a question.
Circle the question mark.

1 Who hid the cat?

2 Can the cat see the rat?

3 The cat is in the van.

4 Can the van go?

Read the sentences. Circle each sentence that asks something.

5 Can we sit in the van?

We can sit in the van.

6 Dan can nap in the van.

Can Dan nap in the van?

Telling Sentences

 A telling sentence tells something.

Draw a line to match each sentence with the picture that shows what the sentence tells.

1 She has a mop.

2 The dog is on top.

3 Dan gets the hats.

4 Ron can clean spots.

Exclamation Sentences

Exclamatory sentences show strong feelings such as excitement, surprise, or fear. They end with exclamation marks. (!)

Read each sentence. Circle each exclamation mark. Draw a line under the capital letter at the beginning of each sentence.

1 Help! The rat is on top!

2 Get the cat!

3 This cat is bad!

4 Uh-oh! The cat is wet!

Read each set of sentences. Draw a line under the sentence or sentences that show strong feeling.

5 Oh my! Get the dog!

Let's get the dog.

6 The dog runs.

Oh! The dog runs!

WRITING

Squeak!

Circle the words that show the correct way to begin each sentence.

1. The mouse / the mouse is looking for food.

2. he finds / He finds a cracker on the floor.

3. he Eats / He eats the cracker.

Counting Sheep

Write the beginning words correctly to make a sentence.

1.  we read
_____
_____

books before bed.

2. then we
_____
_____

hug good night.

3.  my bed
_____
_____

is soft and cozy.

Sweet Dreams!

Write each beginning word correctly to make a sentence.

1. my dog

_____

runs in her sleep.

2. she must

_____

be dreaming.

3. maybe she

_____

is chasing a cat.

The Night Sky

A **telling sentence** *ends with a* **period.**

period

Add a period to each sentence.

1. Many things shine in the sky at night___

2. The moon looks the brightest___

3. It is closest to Earth___

4. The stars look like tiny dots___

5. They are very far away___

Patriotic Sentences

A **sentence** tells a complete idea. It should always make sense.

Color the flag to show:

RED = sentence   WHITE = not a sentence

★ ★ ★ ★ ★ ★	This is a flag.
★ ★ ★ ★ ★	The flag
★ ★ ★ ★ ★ ★	The flag has stars.
★ ★ ★ ★ ★	The stars
★ ★ ★ ★ ★ ★	The stars are white.
★ ★ ★ ★ ★	The stripes
★ ★ ★ ★ ★ ★	The stripes are red.

And white
The stripes are white.
Blue part
The flag has a blue part.
There are
There are 50 stars.

High-Flying Sentences

Color each flag that tells a complete thought. Leave the other flags blank.

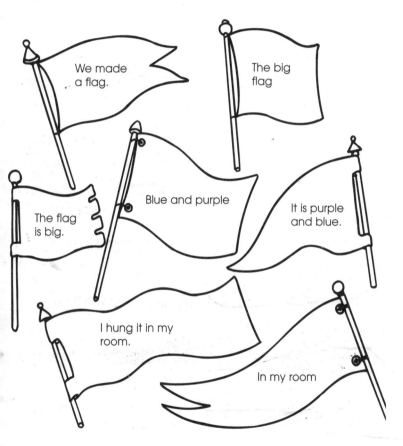

We made a flag.

The big flag

The flag is big.

Blue and purple

It is purple and blue.

I hung it in my room.

In my room

Snakes Alive!

A sentence has a **naming part**. It tells who or what the sentence is about.

Color the snake that tells the naming part in each sentence below.

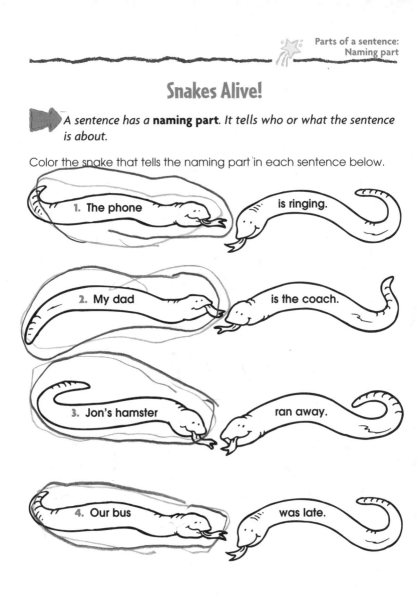

1. The phone   is ringing.

2. My dad   is the coach.

3. Jon's hamster   ran away.

4. Our bus   was late.

Slithering Sentences

Circle the naming part in each sentence below.
Then color the picture to match.

1. The blue snake is playing with a friend.

2. The yellow snake is climbing a tree.

3. The green snake hides under rocks.

4. The brown snake is swimming.

5. The red snake is hanging on a tree.

6. The purple snake sleeps in trees.

7. The black snake rests on a rock.

8. The orange snake is near an egg.

No Bones About It!

A sentence has an **action part**. It tells what is happening.

Color the bone that tells the action part in each sentence below.

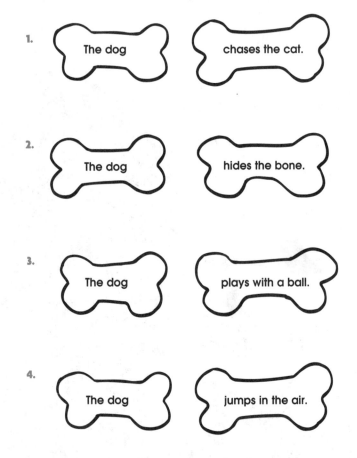

1. The dog   chases the cat.

2. The dog   hides the bone.

3. The dog   plays with a ball.

4. The dog   jumps in the air.

Mighty Good Sentences

Choose the ending that tells what each dog is doing. Remember to use periods.

is eating.

is sleeping.

is jumping.

is barking.

1. The white dog _____ The white dog

2. The gray dog _____ The gray dog

3. The spotted dog _____ The spotted dog

4. The striped dog _____ The striped dog

61

Sensational Words

Choose words from the Word Bank to describe each picture.

It tastes _____.

It looks _____.

It feels _____.

Word Bank

bumpy

crunchy

furry

gray

red

salty

smooth

squeaky

sweet

It feels _____.

It tastes _____.

It sounds _____.

It looks _____.

It sounds _____.

It feels _____.

Pretty Packages

The describing words in a sentence help the reader paint a picture in his or her mind.

Write three words to describe each gift. Then color them to match.

_____ (color)

_____ (color)

_____ (pattern)

_____ (color)

_____ (color)

_____ (pattern)

Keep It in Order

 *Sentences can be written in order to tell a story.*

Finish each story by writing sentences about the last pictures.

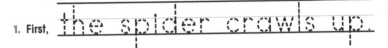

1. **First,** the spider crawls up.

Next, _____

_____

_____

Last, _____

_____

_____

What's Next?

Sentences can be written in order to give directions.

Finish each set of directions by writing sentences about the last pictures.

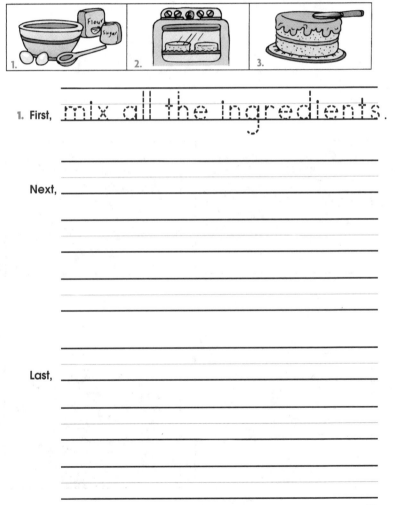

1. First, mix all the ingredients.

Next, _____

_____

_____

_____

_____

Last, _____

_____

_____

_____

Which Title Fits?

*The name of a story is called the **title**. It matches with the story. Most of the words in a title begin with capital letters.*

Match each title with its story. Write the title above the picture.

A Big Beak	**The Big Win**
My Space Friend	**A Knight's Tale**

(title)   (title)

(title)   (title)

MATH

Number User

I use numbers to tell about myself.

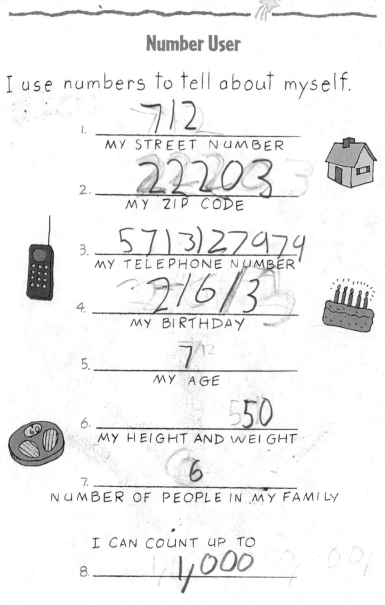

1. __712__
   MY STREET NUMBER

2. __22203__
   MY ZIP CODE

3. __5713127974__
   MY TELEPHONE NUMBER

4. __2/6/3__
   MY BIRTHDAY

5. __7__
   MY AGE

6. __550__
   MY HEIGHT AND WEIGHT

7. __6__
   NUMBER OF PEOPLE IN MY FAMILY

   I CAN COUNT UP TO
8. __1,000__

Flowers in a Pot

Count the dots in the boxes. Then color the matching number word.

Sign Shape

Street signs come in different shapes. Use string to form the shapes below. Work with a partner. Answer the questions below about the shapes, too.

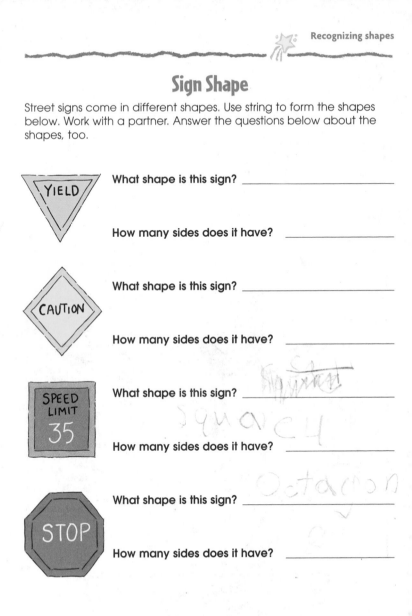

What shape is this sign? _____

How many sides does it have? _____

What shape is this sign? _____

How many sides does it have? _____

What shape is this sign? _____ Triangle

squach

How many sides does it have? _____

Octagon

What shape is this sign? _____

How many sides does it have? _____

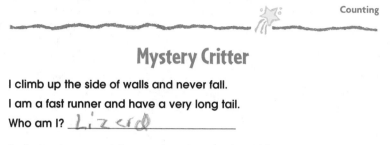

Mystery Critter

I climb up the side of walls and never fall.

I am a fast runner and have a very long tail.

Who am I? _Lizard_

To find out, connect the numbers in order from 20 to 68.

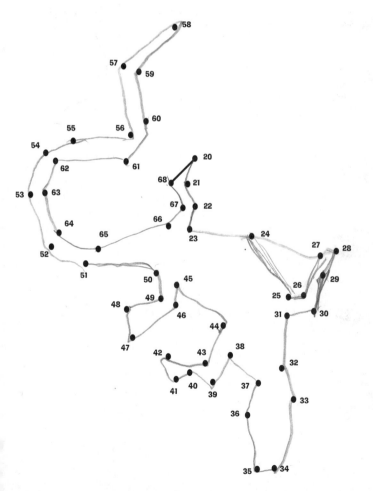

Ladybug Dots

Every year, ladybugs hibernate when the weather gets cool. Count the dots on each ladybug wing. Then write an equation to show the total number of dots each ladybug has. The first one has been done for you.

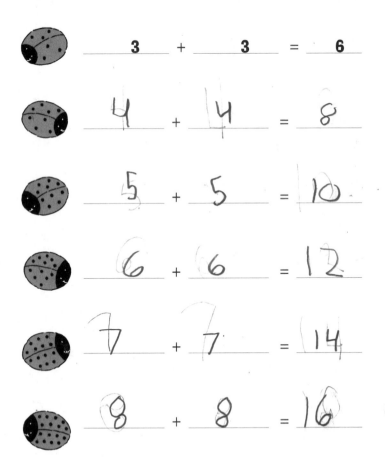

3 + 3 = 6

4 + 4 = 8

5 + 5 = 10

6 + 6 = 12

7 + 7 = 14

8 + 8 = 16

The Truth About the Tooth Fairy

Look at Ali Gator's teeth.

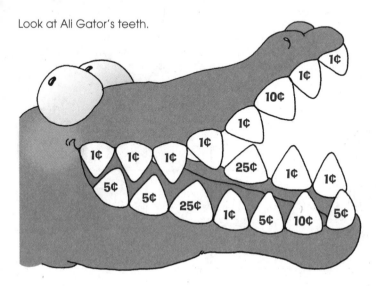

	How many teeth?	How much money in all?
1. How many 1¢?	10	10 cents
2. How many 5¢?	4	20 cents
3. How many 10¢?	2	20 cents
4. How many 25¢?	2	50 cents

Five Senses

We learn about the world by using our 5 senses. The 5 senses are seeing, hearing, smelling, touching, and tasting.

Look at the pictures on the left side of the graph. Think about which of your senses you use to learn about it. Draw a checkmark in the box to show the senses used. (Hint: You might use more than one.)

	See	Hear	Smell	Touch	Taste

December Weather

In December, Mrs. Monroe's class drew the weather on a calendar.
Each kind of weather has a picture:

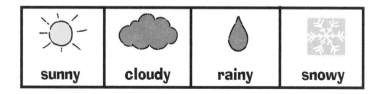

| sunny | cloudy | rainy | snowy |

Look at the calendar. Answer the questions below.

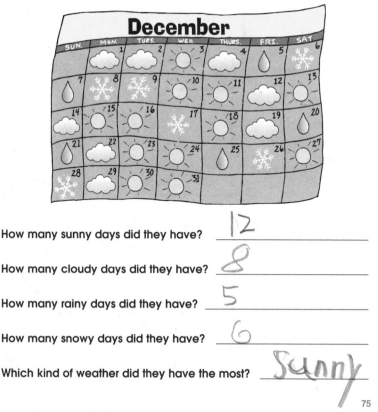

How many sunny days did they have? _____12_____

How many cloudy days did they have? _____8_____

How many rainy days did they have? _____5_____

How many snowy days did they have? _____6_____

Which kind of weather did they have the most? _____Sunny_____

75

Fun With Fractions

 A fraction is a part of a whole.

The shapes below are split into parts, or fractions.
Color only the shapes that are split into equal parts (equal fractions).

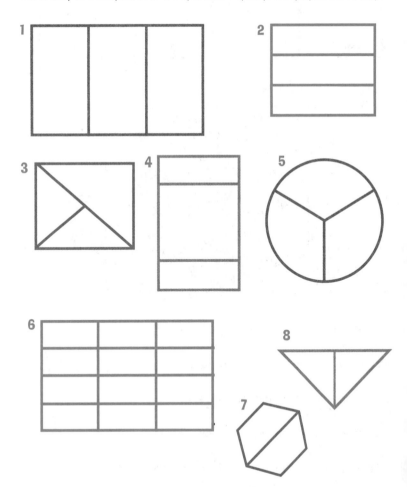

Parts to Color

A fraction has two numbers. The top number will tell you how many parts to color. The bottom number tells you how many parts there are.

Color 1/5 of the circle.

Color 4/5 of the rectangle.

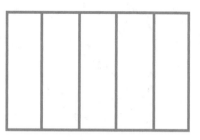

Color 3/5 of the ants.

Color 2/5 of the spiders.

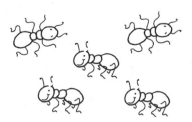

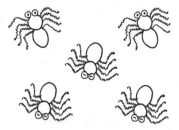

More Parts to Color

A fraction has two numbers. The top number will tell you how many parts to color. The bottom number tells you how many parts there are.

Color 1/8 of the circle.

Color 6/8 of the rectangle.

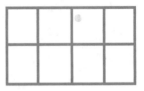

Color 4/8 of the suns.

Color 8/8 of the stars.

Clock Work

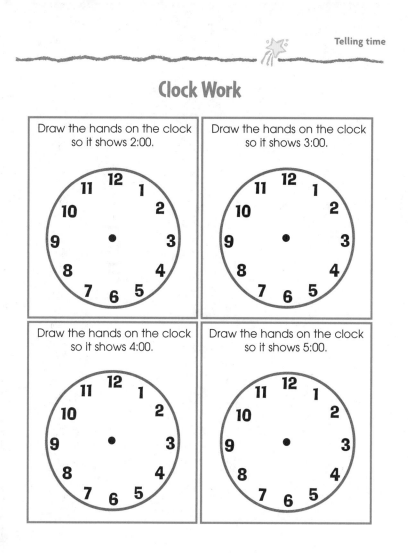

Draw the hands on the clock so it shows 2:00.

Draw the hands on the clock so it shows 3:00.

Draw the hands on the clock so it shows 4:00.

Draw the hands on the clock so it shows 5:00.

More Clock Work

Draw the hands on the clock so it shows 3:00.

Draw the hands on the clock so it shows 6:00.

Draw the hands on the clock so it shows 9:00.

Draw the hands on the clock so it shows 12:00.

Have a Heart

Circle a group of 10. Write the number of tens and ones.

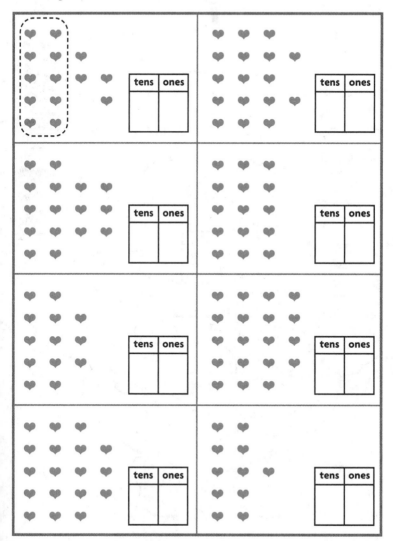

Clowning Around

Add. Color the picture
using the color code.

Color Code

1	pink
2	white
3	black
4	brown
5	purple
6	green
7	blue
8	orange
9	yellow
10	red

5 + 2 =

6 + 3 =

4
+ 5

5
+ 0

7
+ 2

4
+ 4

2
+ 3

2 + 5 =

3 + 2 =

4
+ 3

3
+ 3

1
+ 0

4
+ 2

0
+ 1

5
+ 1

4 + 1 =

6
+ 2

2
+ 1

3
+ 0

3
+ 5

7 + 0 =

5 + 5 =

6 + 1 =

1
+ 1

7 + 3 =

3 + 1 =

Lovely Ladybugs

Write a number sentence to show how many spots each ladybug has.

Juggling Act

Cross out. Write how many are left.

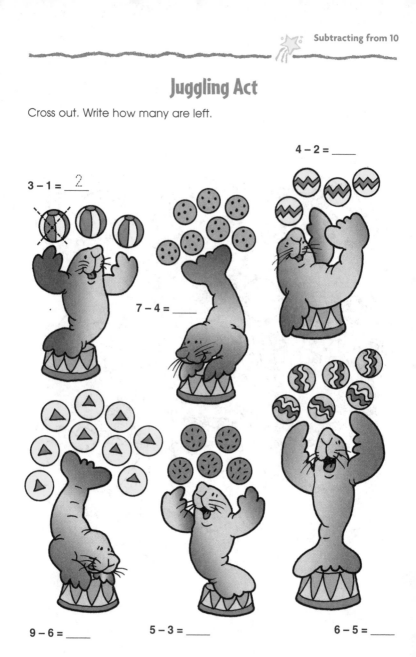

4 − 2 = _____

3 − 1 = _2_

7 − 4 = _____

9 − 6 = _____

5 − 3 = _____

6 − 5 = _____

Mitten Matchup

Add or subtract. Draw a line to match mittens with the same answer.

Out on the Town

Color a box on the graph for each item in the picture.

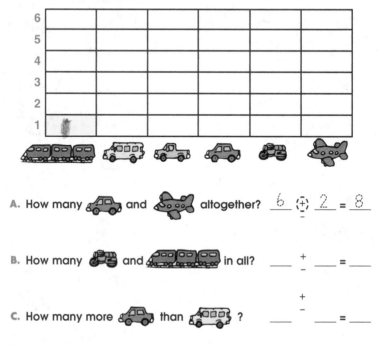

A. How many 🚗 and ✈️ altogether? $\underline{6}$ (+) $\underline{2}$ = $\underline{8}$

B. How many 🏍️ and 🚃 in all? $\underline{}$ + $\underline{}$ = $\underline{}$

C. How many more 🚗 than 🚐 ? $\underline{}$ + $\underline{}$ = $\underline{}$

Leap on Over

Add. To show the frog's path across the pond, color each lily pad green if the sum is greater than 10.

10 + 1 =

6 + 4 =

6 + 9 =

5 + 2 =

7 + 0 =

5 + 5 =

9 + 2 =

10 + 4 =

3 + 7 =

7 + 6 =

4 + 3 =

5 + 4 =

3 + 8 =

2 + 2 =

8 + 8 =

Animal Mystery

What kind of animal always carries a trunk?

_____

To find out, solve the addition problems. If the answer is greater than 9, color the shape yellow. If the answer is less than 10, color the shape gray.

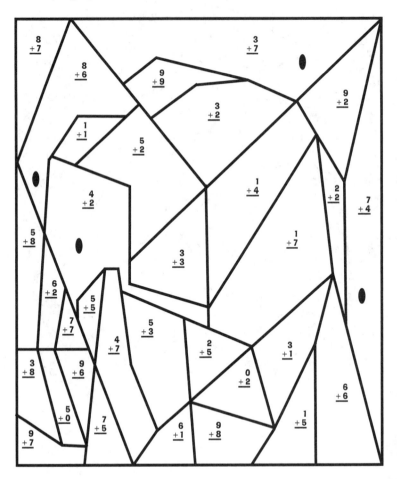

Double Dips

Write the doubles that equal the number on the cone.

Flying Families

Fill in the missing number for each family. Use the numbers from the box.

9	12	15	8	10
6	4	7	5	11	2

Colorful Flowers

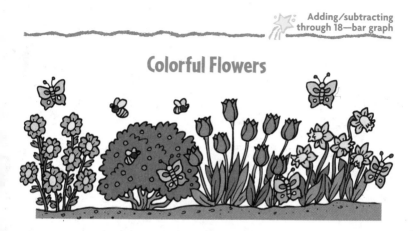

Color a box on the graph for each item in the picture.

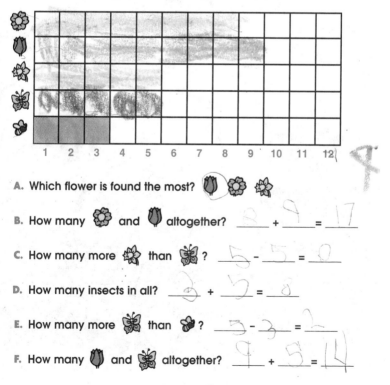

A. Which flower is found the most?

B. How many 🌼 and 🌷 altogether? _____ 8 + _____ 9 = _____ 17

C. How many more 🌸 than 🦋 ? _____ 5 - _____ 5 = _____ 0

D. How many insects in all? _____ 3 + _____ 5 = _____ 8

E. How many more 🦋 than 🐝 ? _____ 5 - _____ 3 = _____ 2

F. How many 🌷 and 🦋 altogether? _____ 9 + _____ 5 = _____ 14

91

By the Seashore

Use the code below to write each missing number. Add.

Number Buddies

Subtract. Remember: the largest number always goes on top!

A. 7 39

3 9
– 7

B. 54 1

–

C. 87 6

–

D. 73 3

–

Color the Sunflower

Do the addition problems in the sunflower
picture below. Then use the Color Key to tell
you what color to make each answer.

Extra: Write your age on four flashcards, and
then add a 6, 7, 8, and 9 to each of the cards.
Practice the answers with a friend.

| **Color Key** |
| 56 = green |
| 68 = orange |
| 89 = yellow |
| 97 = blue |

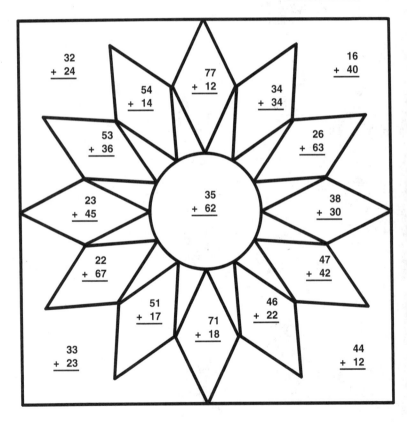

```
  32              16
+ 24            + 40
      54   77   34
    + 14 + 12 + 34
  53              26
+ 36            + 63
         35
  23   + 62     38
+ 45            + 30
  22              47
+ 67            + 42
    51     46
  + 17   + 22
       71
     + 18
  33              44
+ 23            + 12
```

Have a Ball

Subtract.

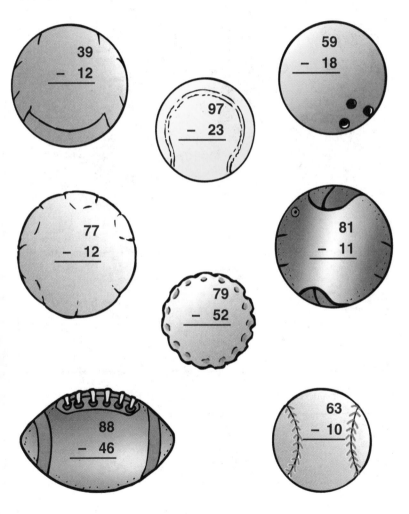

$$\begin{array}{r} 39 \\ -\ 12 \\ \hline \end{array}$$

$$\begin{array}{r} 59 \\ -\ 18 \\ \hline \end{array}$$

$$\begin{array}{r} 97 \\ -\ 23 \\ \hline \end{array}$$

$$\begin{array}{r} 77 \\ -\ 12 \\ \hline \end{array}$$

$$\begin{array}{r} 81 \\ -\ 11 \\ \hline \end{array}$$

$$\begin{array}{r} 79 \\ -\ 52 \\ \hline \end{array}$$

$$\begin{array}{r} 88 \\ -\ 46 \\ \hline \end{array}$$

$$\begin{array}{r} 63 \\ -\ 10 \\ \hline \end{array}$$

How Much Money?

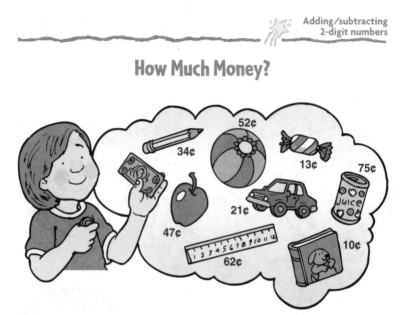

Add to find out how much.

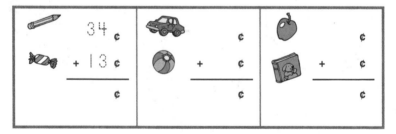

Subtract to find out how much.

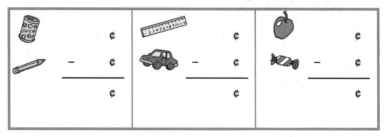